HOUGHTON MIFFLIN
Reading
A Legacy of Literacy

Silly Stories

Len and Linda's Picnic

by Becky Ward
illustrated by Mona Daly

Linda sat with her chin in her hand.

"I can't think of a game to play," she said sadly.

Ring, ring, ring, went the bell. Ring, ring, ring.

"Someone has come to visit," thought Linda.

1

Linda went to her front door.

"My best pal Len! I am glad you came to visit. I need a game to play," said Linda.

"You are in luck," said Len. "I just bought a new ball. We can roll it and catch it. It will be fun."

Drip, drip, drip went the rain. Drip, drip, drip. But Len and Linda's picnic did not get wet.

2

7

"Linda," yelled Len. "Come see. You will think this game is fun."

Linda looked and looked until she found Len in the den.

"Look at this! It's an indoor picnic!" said Len.

Linda jumped up and down with glee.

Just then, big drops of rain started falling.

"We can't play outside when it is raining," said Linda. "This is a sad, sad day."

Len sat down on the steps to think. Soon he said, "I know just what we need to make this sad day fun!"

6

3

big basket
cloth
plates
napkins
plastic cups
tea
jam
toast

Len went to the kitchen. He got a pad and a pen and made this list.

Len found the things on his list. Linda packed them in the big basket. Len took the basket and left.

Linda looked at the rain on the window. "This wet day is no fun. We can't picnic until it stops raining."

4

5

4A

An Ice Cream Crash

by Becky Ward

illustrated by S. Signorino

Will and Jill were feeling hungry.
The twins looked in the kitchen. Jill
looked high. Will looked low. Then Will
and Jill looked at each other.
"No ice cream," said Jill.

9

"We can ride to town and get ice cream," said Will.

"Let's get going," said Jill.

Will and Jill jumped on their bike and started down the steep hill to Bob's Food Store in town.

10

Sam took the twins home.

"Crashing into an ice cream truck is not fun," said Will.

"But eating ice cream IS!" added Jill.

15

"Too bad," said Sam, as he helped Will
and Jill get up. "Maybe this will make
you feel better."

Sam reached into the back of his truck
and handed each twin an ice cream cone.

Down, down, down the hill they rolled.
Zoom! Zoom! Zoom! They could not
stop. Until . . . bump, crash, boom. Their
trip ended fast.

14

11

"We bumped into a truck," said Will.
"And we bumped it hard," added Jill.
"Help us, please!" yelled the twins.

12

Sam rushed from his truck. "What is this?" he asked.

"We went looking for ice cream and rolled down that hill fast. We bumped into this truck," said Jill.

"My knee is scratched," said Will, starting to cry.

13

Big Hog's House Hunt

by Melissa Blackwell Burke

illustrated by Deborah Melmon

Big Hog was looking for a new home when he met Hot Dog.

"It's my job to help pals look for new homes," said Hot Dog. "It just so happens that at the present time, I have seven homes for sale. I bet I can sell you a home!"

"Let's hop on it," said Big Hog.

17

Big Hog and Hot Dog set off on a house hunt. Hot Dog led Big Hog to a grand web.

"It's a special web, near the bus stop and the vet. It's extra big. Do you like it a lot or not, Big Hog?"

18

"Yes! Yes!" said Hot Dog. "Surprise! This is a special pen. It has lots of mud and lots of space. Do you like it a lot or not, Big Hog?"

"Yes! I will take it," said Big Hog. "It is just right. Welcome to my new home, Hot Dog! Visit me any time."

He hugged Hot Dog. "Good job," said Big Hog. "You found the right home for me."

23

But Hot Dog and Big Hog did not set off.

"Let me think," said Hot Dog. "Not a web. Not a den. We'll keep on looking. We can see five more homes. I will not give up yet."

All of a sudden, Big Hog hopped up. "Such fun! You brought me here for a reason, Hot Dog."

22

"No," said Big Hog. "A web is not a good home for a hog. A web gets too much sun, and it's not big enough."

"Not a problem," said Hot Dog. "We'll keep on looking."

"Let's hop on it," said Big Hog.

19

Big Hog and Hot Dog went down the road. Hot Dog led Big Hog to a cub's den.

"It's a fine den. It is dark, and it is extra, extra big. It will make a good home for you. Do you like it a lot or not, Big Hog?"

"No," said Big Hog. "A den might be good for a cub, but it's not the right home for me. A den does not get enough sun, and it is much too big."

"Not a problem," said Hot Dog. "We'll keep on looking."

"Let's hop on it," said Big Hog.

20

21

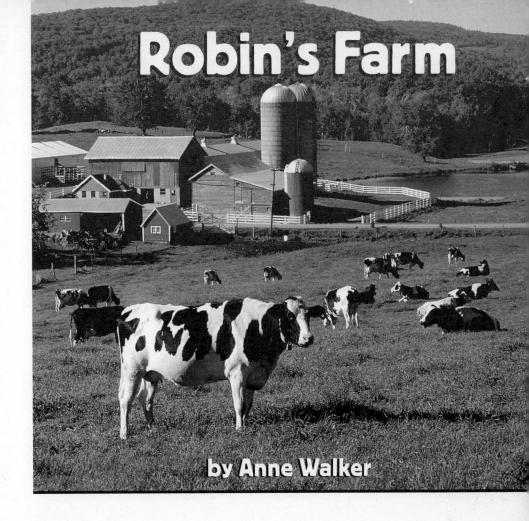

Robin's Farm

by Anne Walker

Many animals live on Robin's farm in New York.

Cows graze on green grass. Late in the day the cows go inside for milking.

25

Robin's cat is named Jazz. It has striped fur with a big white spot. It takes naps in a basket.

At night Jazz catches mice in the barn.

26

The pigs stay warm at night. They sleep in the barn with Agnes.

Robin closes the barn door, and then she smiles.

"Good night, new pals. Good night, Agnes."

31

Robin had a special surprise this spring. Her pig Agnes gave birth to six piglets. Agnes takes good care of her six brand new babies.

Robin's white rabbit hops about in a large rabbit hutch.

The rabbit's pink ears stand up when Robin brings food.

30

27

Robin's dog Flash rides in Robin's old red pickup truck.

Flash sticks his head out the window. They ride to the feed store to get feed for Robin's horses.

A hen sat on three brown eggs in the hen house.

Now three new chicks will play with Flash.

28

29

Jane's Mistake

by Patty Moynahan
illustrated by Marsha Winborn

Jane Crane has a nice smile, but Jane
is not wearing a smile now. Her bracelet
is missing.

Did someone take Jane's bracelet?

33

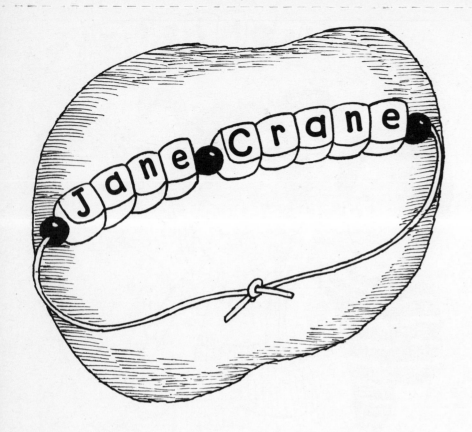

"I made my bracelet," said Jane. "It has a bead for each letter in my name. Who might take my bracelet with JANE CRANE on it? Whoever took it might switch the letters and spell a different name — like ACE RENNA or ENJAN RACE!"

"You poor thing!" said Jane.

Just then Miss Fine came in. She had found Jane's bracelet on a hall floor.

"Thanks," said Jane. Then Jane looked at Kate. "From now on, I will try to be more kind."

Kate gave Jane a big smile.

34

39

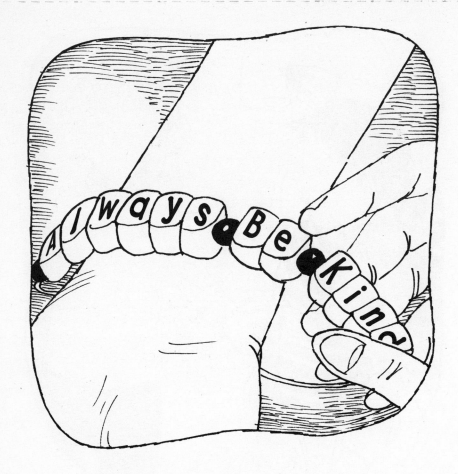

Jane read each word on Kate's bracelet.

The beads did not spell JANE CRANE. They spelled ALWAYS BE KIND.

Jane's face turned red.

"Look!" shouted Jake. "Kate has a bead bracelet. It might be your bracelet, Jane. Let's ask her if it is. Quick! We must move fast."

38

35

The kids began to chase Kate.

"I think that's my bracelet!"
yelled Jane.

Kate looked at them. Then she
went inside the gym.

"Don't try to hide!" yelled Jane.

Kate stopped. Jane and her friends
also stopped.

"This bracelet is mine," said Kate.
She held out her arm.

36

37

The Big Surprise

by Patty Moynahan
illustrated by Ruth Flanigan

Mom and Pop Lane live in a big red house. Six Lane children live in the big red house, too.

One fine day, Mom and Pop went on a trip.

"See you soon!" said Mom and Pop.

"Have fun, Mom and Pop!"

41

"Let's surprise Mom and Pop," said Big Sis. "We can clean the house — up and down, inside and out."

Sis gave each child a job. "Ben, you mop. Take this bucket. Dot, you help Bob make the beds. Wait until Mom and Pop see this spotless home!"

42

"Look!" said Bob. "It's Mom and Pop!"
"Surprise! Surprise!
We cleaned the house, Mom and Pop!
This mess is a surprise to us!"

47

22A

"Such a mess!" said Sis.
"What will Mom and Pop say?"

Sis swept the halls. Ned dusted.
Todd scrubbed the windows.

46

43

At last the house was clean.

"Good work, kids!" said Sis. "Mom
and Pop will be proud."

Then Sis gave them hugs.

Sis, Ben, Dot, Bob, Ned, and Todd slept
well. They dreamed sweet dreams.
They did not know what Dot forgot.
Dot forgot to close the windows!

44

45

Nature Walk

HOUGHTON MIFFLIN

Reading

A Legacy of Literacy

Miss Pig's Garden

by Patty Moynahan   illustrated by John Gurney

Miss Pig would like a garden this year.

"I will plant a big garden filled with beautiful roses," said Miss Pig.

1

Miss Pig started digging her garden.
Mule came to look.

"I might even win a prize," said Miss
Pig. "This garden will be large. It will
be grand!"

Miss Pig got her beautiful garden
back. She was happy.

She gave Pete Goat his own garden.
Now he can take all the roses he wants.

2

7

Pete was quiet. Then he looked sad. "I will make it up to you," he said. "I will plant new roses in this garden."

The village came to see Miss Pig's garden.

To Frog, it looked huge.

"Such straight rows!" barked Dog.

When Dog and Frog left, Miss Pig stood alone in her yard. She felt happy.

6

3B

3

At night, Pete Goat came to Miss Pig's garden. He had his wagon with him.

"Just look at these roses!" said Pete Goat. He started to pick the roses and put them in his wagon.

Miss Pig awoke the next morning.

"My beautiful garden!" she said. "Who could be so rude?"

She went to see Pete Goat.

"I know that goats like to eat roses," said Miss Pig. "Did you eat my roses, Pete?"

4

5

Mike and Dave Sleep Outside

by Patty Moynahan
illustrated by Patrick Joseph

Mike and Dave sat on the porch.

A big smile was on Mike's face.

"Why are you smiling?" asked Dave.

"I have an idea!" shouted Mike. "You will like this plan."

9

"We can pitch a tent by that fish pond," said Mike.

"The side yard can be dark woods. That pond can be our lake. We can take a hike. We can ride bikes. Then we can make something to eat."

10

The next day Mike and Dave took down their tent. The wind was blowing.

"Reek! Reek!"

Mike and Dave looked at each other. Then they looked at the gate. The wind was blowing it back and forth.

"Reek! Reek!"

"It was just that creaky old gate!" shouted Mike and Dave.

15

"I don't feel safe outside," shouted
Mike.

He yelled, "Mom! Dad!"

Soon Mike's dad came out.

He took Mike and Dave back to the
house. They went to sleep in Mike's room.

14

Mike and Dave played baseball
that day.

They went hiking.

Then they made hotdogs on the grill.

Mike's dad made sure the fire went out
before he went inside.

11

Mike's mom gave the boys a big flashlight.

"Don't stay up late," she said.

The boys talked and played games until bedtime.

Then Mike and Dave went to sleep.

"Mike, wake up!" yelled Dave. "Did you hear that sound?"

Mike's eyes opened wide.

Dave saw Mike nod.

"Reek! Reek!" went that sound.

12

13

A Trip to Central Park

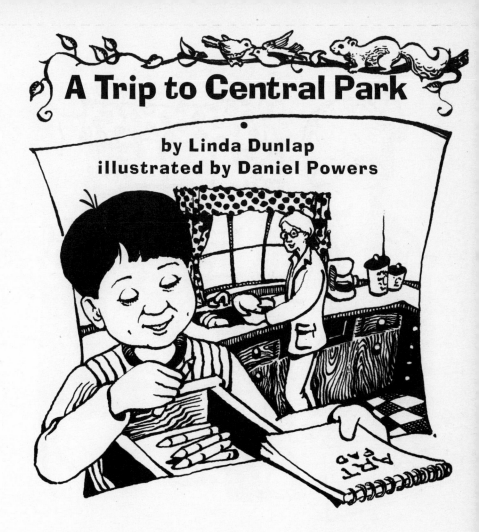

by Linda Dunlap
illustrated by Daniel Powers

"It's an important day," exclaims
Gran.

"We start exploring Central Park!"
Gran and I get busy. I decide to bring
pencils so I can make drawings.

17

Gran plans a neat surprise. It's a
secret treat she's saving for later.

Gran packs her small plastic food
basket. She makes the best picnics!

18

Gran smiles. It's time for my
surprise.

She takes thick, sweet cream cakes
from the small plastic basket.

Sweet cream cakes make good treats!
And a trip to Central Park makes this
day fun!

23

We can eat now! Gran opens the small plastic basket. The food smells good! Gran likes sweet grape jam. I take bread, sliced ham, crisp chips, and fresh grapes.

We walk down stone trails in the park.

Big and small plants grow on the edges. Spring bushes are blooming.

Huge trees make cool shade and nice breezes blow.

22

19

I draw trees. I include frogs, snakes, and trees in my drawing. I make them green. I draw clouds that touch the sky. Gran is pleased with my art.

20

We find a nice, grassy picnic spot. It is near the bridge and playground.
I lay blankets on the ground to sit on. We watch young children playing games.

21

12B

Zeke and Pete Rule!

by Linda Dunlap
illustrated by John Lund

Zeke the farm mule got a flute. He played notes and made tunes. But he played tunes alone. Zeke hoped to make pals. He hated playing alone!

25

Pete the Pig went by Zeke's place.
"I hear a cute tune," said Pete.
Zeke smiled. "Will you sit and stay,
Pete?"

26

Zeke and Pete chose a nice, secret
home. It had wading ponds and quiet
places.

Pete planted roses. Zeke played flute
tunes. In this place, Pete and Zeke did
rule!

31

Zeke and Pete became huge stars. Ropes held back crowds when they played. But Zeke missed farm life. Pete hoped for quiet time.

Zeke and Pete needed a rest.

Soon, Pete and Zeke became close pals. Zeke played cute tunes. Pete danced. People liked to watch Zeke and Pete.

30

27

Zeke wrote new songs. Pete
made new dances.

"Pete rules!" joked Zeke.

"Zeke rules!" Pete exclaimed.

Tunes from Zeke's flute drew crowds
of people. Pete's exciting dancing made
them stay. People pressed close to watch
and hear.

"Excuse us," Zeke said.

"Please make space!" exclaimed Pete.

28

29

In the Woods

by Becky Ward

illustrated by Neecy Twinem

Who is at home where tall trees grow?
Can you tell? Let's look in the woods
and see.

33

Can you see that hill of grass? A
mother made a safe place and stacked
grass over her children. Pick up the
grass and look. It is a brown rabbit and
her brother!

34

Mammals, fish, birds, and bugs — all
these animals are at home in the woods!

39

Look down in that hole. It is a small den. Get back quickly if you hear loud hissing and feet stamping. That means a mad skunk will soon spray its bad smell!

Splish! Splash! A fish is jumping and splashing across the stream. It is a big bass catching bugs for lunch.

38

35

Look out! Check that hollow stump for yellow jackets. Yellow jackets chew plants and make paper. Then they use it to make a nest in the ground, in a tree, or in a hollow log. The yellow jacket queen fills the nest with eggs.

36

Shhh! Stand as still as can be and look up in that willow tree. It's the great horned owl! This strong bird hunts for rabbits and chickens. It nests on cliffs or in big trees.

37

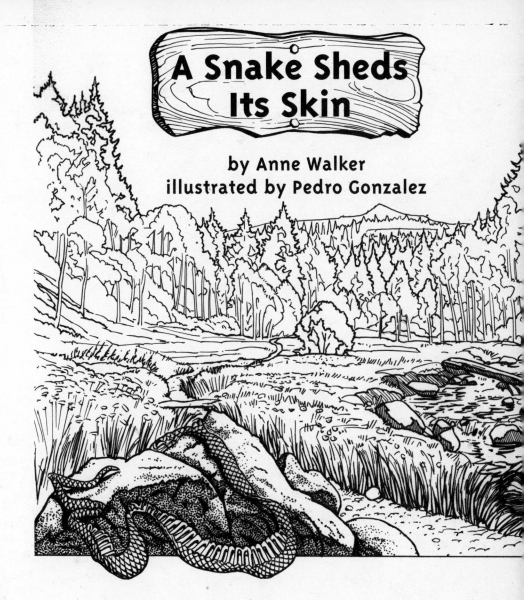

A Snake Sheds Its Skin

by Anne Walker
illustrated by Pedro Gonzalez

If you go on a hike in the park and look around, you might see a snake's skin.

41

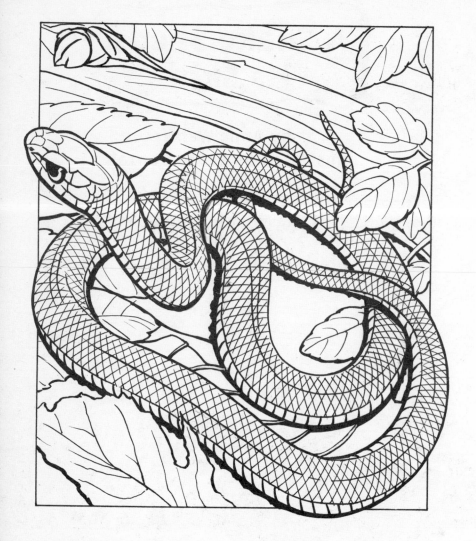

A snake's skin cannot grow. As a young snake grows, its skin gets tight. Then it is time for the snake to shed its skin.

As it grows, the snake will outgrow this new skin too. Then it will be time for this snake to shed its skin again.

42

47

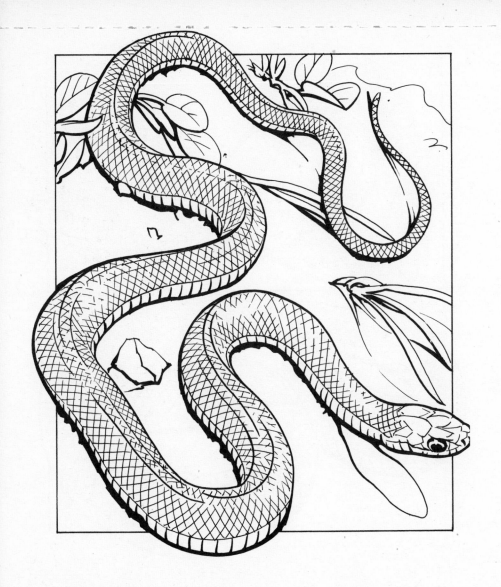

The snake's new skin is dry and smooth and nice to touch. Its scales help the snake slide smoothly on the ground.

The snake looks for a safe place. Then it rubs its nose on something hard, like a rock or a stick. The skin splits and peels away from the snake's body.

46

43

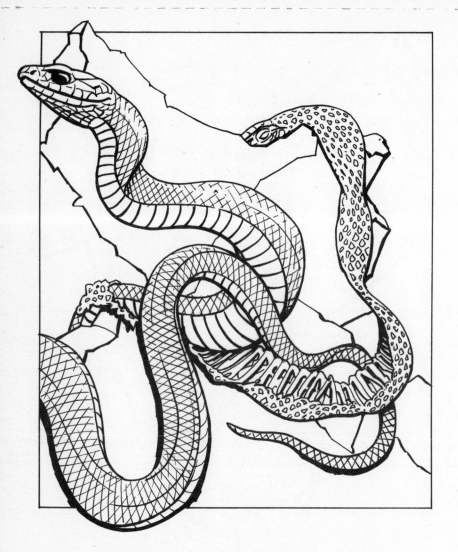

The snake keeps rubbing. It slides out of its tight skin. The old skin is left inside out, like a glove when you take your hand out.

Underneath its peeling skin, this snake has a new skin that fits just right.

44

45

HOUGHTON MIFFLIN
Reading
A Legacy of Literacy

Around Town:

Neighborhood and Community

Sunshine for the Circus

by Linda Dunlap
illustrated by Sarah Dillard

During winter, this town makes room
for new friends. The circus visits!
Sunshine and beaches make circus
people want to stay and play. Days get
hotter. This means they can practice
and play outside.

1

Circus families work and play. Moms and dads teach little children. Each person practices and plays hard.

2

Last night, a loud noise shook this house. A family dashed outside. The moon looked bright. The stars looked brighter.

In a flash, the family knew what they had heard. A loud lion sounded louder than thunder! With the circus in town, life can be exciting!

7

The biggest cats do not get baths. The biggest cats just get brushed and fed.

It's time to feed this lion fresh meat. Do you think they will brush his teeth?

6

They practice exciting circus acts. Cheerful boys turn big cartwheels. Men swing far up. Arms and hands reach out and catch. It's the neatest show!

3

3C

Other days, circus families choose to rest. Groups make the short trip to Shell Beach.

Moms and dads shop at beach stores. Kids fish, splash, and hunt shells.

Circus families spend much time each day with animals. Horses splash in water and then shake it off. Three horses are bigger than the others. The little horses are the cutest! A man checks each horse's feet and legs.

4

5

Mother's Day Parade on Park Street

by Linda Dunlap
illustrated by R.W. Alley

Park Street children love parades.
We look for excuses to plan them.

9

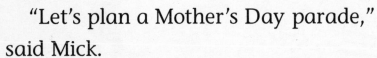

"Let's plan a Mother's Day parade,"
said Mick.

"That's great!" Jill exclaimed. "What
shall we plan?"

"Let me think," Mick said. Then he
shouted, "A pet parade! We will march
down Park Street with our pets!"

All the children liked that. Each
began to think of ways to show pets.

10

On Mother's Day, Park Street
children got together. Moms, dads,
grandmothers, and grandfathers lined
the block.

Nell thumped beats on her drum. Kids
and willing pets marched around the
block. Groups watched and yelled
greetings to passing children.

What a swell Mother's Day parade!

15

Mick had still another problem. Mick's problem was his pet, Chuck Chicken. Chickens will not stay in line for long!

Mick went to the pet shop. Way in back, he found a tiny leash.

"Will you sell me this?" Mick asked Miss Black.

"Yes, I will sell it. Let me put it in a sack," Miss Black added.

Mick could use the leash to lead Chuck Chicken.

14

Bess made yellow stockings and shoes for her pup. First she cut yellow cloth. Then she stitched it.

The costume looked great!

11

Latisha picked buckets of fresh
flowers. She planned to make a flower
sash for her sheep.

Then Latisha yelled, "What a mess!"
She found out that sheep chew flowers!

Latisha made another plan. Her
sheep would march in Dad's old slacks.
Dad was willing to help.

Jill had a pet fish. How could she
show a fish? Fish can't march. Fish can't
dress up.

Jill had an idea. She put a little
mattress in Mick's wagon. Then she
placed the fish bowl on the mattress.
She polished the fish bowl, making
it shine.

12

13

Jay the Mailman

by Melissa Blackwell Burke
illustrated by Tom Stanley

Jay has brought mail to people for years. Jay checks that everything is in order. This is Jay's last day.

17

As Jay stops at shops and homes, people say nice things.

"You are such a good mailman," people say. "It will not be the same without you. Snow or rain could not keep you away."

"Such high praise!" laughs Jay. "No, rain can't stop the mail."

18

The next day, it rains. Jay takes his notes to the mailbox. He is not in his mailman clothes. On his way, he meets Ed and Kay.

"And why are you out in this rain?" Kay asks.

"Rain still can't stop the mail!" explains Jay.

23

10C

Everyone visits and eats until sunset.

"Good luck, Jay the Mailman,"
people say.

Jay waves at them. "Maybe I'll see
you soon."

At home, Jay writes everyone nice
notes. He knows just where he will mail
them.

22

Jay gets handshakes. A cute baby in a
playpen waves. Big dogs wag big tails.

"We will miss you," people say. "Don't
stay away."

19

At the end of this day, Jay makes his last stop. He's a bit sad. He puts mail in the last mailbox. He looks up. It's quiet and then . . . SURPRISE!

Everyone has been waiting inside for him.

20

In the back yard, the fun begins.

"Did you guess?" Ed asks.

"No way!" Jay exclaims.

"How will you spend your time now?" Kay asks.

"I may sail and take train trips," Jay explains. "I may stay home and play with my grandchildren. And, I'll check my mail each day!"

21

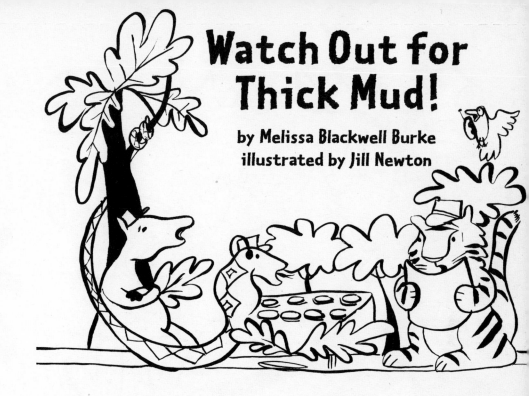

Watch Out for Thick Mud!

by Melissa Blackwell Burke

illustrated by Jill Newton

Things were slow that day at Rain Forest 911.

Mitch and Beth were not doing much of anything. Just then, a call came in. Rich picked up the line.

"This is Rain Forest 911. Who is it? Do you need help?" Rich asked.

"This is Josh. Sasha needs help. She's in a pit. She's stuck in thick mud!"

25

"Help is on the way," Rich said.
"Mitch and Beth will be right there.
Look for them."

"Watch out for thick mud!" Josh
exclaimed.

26

"Stuck?" Sasha asked. "Well, thanks
very much, but I wish you would have
checked with me first. I'm not quite
finished with my mud bath."

With that, Sasha flipped back into the
thick mud with a splash, splash, splash!

"Watch out for thick mud!" Josh
exclaimed.

31

Beth, Mitch, and Josh poked and pulled.   And then, Sasha went "Whoosh!" Thick mud splashed everywhere, and Sasha sat up.

"Watch out for thick mud!" Josh exclaimed.

"What's going on?" Sasha asked.

"You got stuck in thick mud," Beth explained. "So Josh got Rain Forest 911."

30

Beth and Mitch grabbed their things and rushed to help Sasha. When they got near the mud pit, they spotted Josh and jumped out of the van.

"Show us the way fast, Josh," Mitch said.

Josh flew up high to show them the way. Mitch and Beth ran through the brush.

27

When Mitch and Beth got to the mud pit, they were so shocked. Yes, Sasha was stuck in that thick mud. She was stuck head first!

"Rain Forest 911 is here, Sasha," Beth said. "We'll get you out of that thick mud in just a while."

Sasha just made a splash with her trunk.

"Watch out for thick mud!" Josh exclaimed.

Mitch got out ropes and other things.

"What do you think?" Mitch asked. "Shall we try to pull her out with ropes or push her out with poles?"

"Let's try both," Beth said. "You use ropes. We'll use poles."

"Watch out for thick mud!" Josh exclaimed.

28

29

Mouse's Crowded House

by Becky Ward
illustrated by Beth Buffington

"Ouch," said Mouse Mom. "Who bounced that big ball in this house?" But no one could hear her.

She looked at her children . . . so many mice to count. They were so loud that it sounded like a thousand mice playing in the house!

33

Mice bounded loudly down the steps.
Mice bounced on the bed. One mouse
played soldier with the lampshade.
Mice left wet towels in the bathroom.
They spilled jam behind the couch. It
made Mouse Mom feel like a grouch.

Mouse Mom felt glad as she watched
her children run and play. "This house
is not so crowded," she thought. "Now,
this house is just right."

34

39

"My, my! How nice!" said Mom proudly. And she kissed each mouse.

Then she said sweetly, "Don't stay outside. Please go back inside and play."

So they crowded back in and joyful sounds filled the house.

38

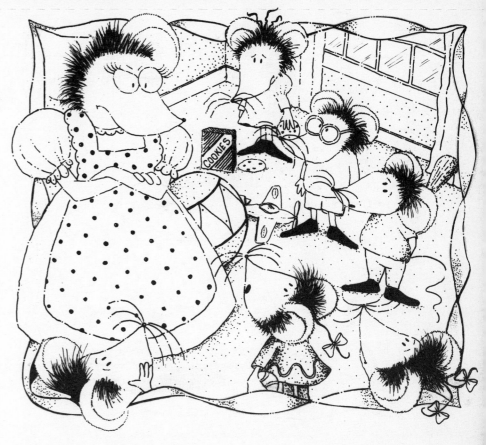

Suddenly Mouse Mom shouted, "No loud sounds allowed! This house is too crowded. Please, go outside NOW!"

The mice fell silent and looked at Mom's frowning face. Without a sound, they picked up their toys and sadly went outside.

35

Mouse Mom sat down on the couch. Her house seemed so peaceful. "This is exactly what I like," thought Mouse Mom. "I'll just sit and think."

But it was lonely. Mouse Mom could only think about her children.

Mouse Mom missed those loud, playful mice. She looked out her window. Were they bouncing and bounding and clowning?

No, that's not what she found! Big Mouse was reading a story, and the rest were seated next to him on the ground.

36

37

Hooray for Main Street
by Becky Ward   illustrated by Doreen Gay-Kassel

"Ray," said Gail, "do you think this town is nice?"

"It's not bad," said Ray.

"Well, I think it is just plain dull," said Gail with a frown.

41

After thinking for a bit, Ray said, "It does not have to stay that way."

"Explain what you mean," said Gail.

"Well, maybe we can make it nice. We can get everyone to help us fix up Main Street," Ray said.

"I like what you're saying. Let's make a plan!" exclaimed Gail.

42

"Now this town is very nice," said Ray. "It is not plain or dull."

"I'll say!" exclaimed Gail. "Now this town makes us proud. It is as nice as it can be!"

Then everyone in town stood up and shouted out loud, "Hooray for Main Street! Hip! Hip! Hooray!"

47

The mayor made Sunday a big day. He praised the new Main Street with its rainbow of flowers. He praised Gail and Ray and those who had helped them. Then the band played while everyone marched down Main Street. Gail and Ray proudly led the way.

Gail and Ray got red and blue crayons and wrote on a big, white box. They made a nice display for people in town to read. Ray drew flowers and Gail wrote the words.

This is what Gail wrote on the box: *Stop and chat with Gail and Ray. Let's find a way to make Main Street nice.*

46

43

Gail and Ray took the display to town. The children waited for people to stop and chat. Gail explained that they needed paint and nails and tools and flowers. Ray made a list of names and wrote down things each person would bring.

The next day, the town started fixing up Main Street. Moms and dads sawed and nailed while children painted and planted. Everyone stayed and helped until daylight was gone. Gail and Ray thanked them for helping.

44

45

The Clean Team

by Anne Walker

illustrated by Daniel Powers

Mike knew he should be cleaning his room.

But he was reading such a good book! It told about a lady who ruled a land near the sea. This queen looked silly but she did lots of neat tricks.

Mike turned the page to read more.

49

Then Mike's mom opened his door. "Mike, we will leave for the park in ten minutes," she told him. "The town cookout starts at noon. You may join us if your room is clean."

50

Mike had fun at the cookout. He ate hot dogs and peach pie. He flew a kite. But the cookout was not the best part of Mike's day. It was cleaning up with the clean team.

55

26C

Soon Mike's whole room was as neat as a pin. Mike could not believe his eyes. "Each toy is away," he said.

"All the furniture is clean," said Jean. "We make a good team!"

54

Mike looked around. His room was a real mess. Toys peeked out from under his bed. Heaps of jeans lay on the floor. Pictures he had made were left about.

Mike got down on his knees. He reached under the bed for a small boat. Then he heard an odd sound.

"Knock! Knock! Scratch! Scratch!"

51

Mike glanced up. He saw Jean and their dog Queen standing near the door.

"We will help clean your room," said Jean. "We can make cleaning up fun."

"Wow! Thanks, Jean," said Mike.

52

"We will be a team," said Jean.

"The clean team," said Mike.

Then she and Mike began to clean up the mess. Even Queen got in on the action. When she picked up a ball, Mike said, "Thanks, Queen! You're such a sweet lady!"

53

28C

Big Hound's Lunch

by Anne Walker
illustrated by Ilene Richards

Mom handed Anna a sack.

"Please take this sack to Dad. His lunch is in it," she said.

Anna took the sack and skipped out of the house.

57

Anna's brown dog bounded up to her.

"It is time to take Dad his lunch, Big Hound," Anna said. She put a leash on Big Hound and they set off. Big Hound took the sack.

"Great!" Anna shouted. "May we go to Sprouts? It is our special place."

Big Hound wagged his tail. He loved to go to lunch.

58

63

30C

Anna and Big Hound reached Dad's store. Anna kissed Dad. She said, "Dad! We brought your lunch."

Then Anna saw that Big Hound was eating Dad's lunch. "Big Hound!" she said. "That lunch was for Dad."

"Well," Dad said. "We can go out to eat."

62

Mister Trout waved from his mail truck. Anna waved back. Big Hound wagged the lunch sack at Mister Trout.

Anna smiled. "Big Hound!" she said. "That lunch is for Dad!"

59

Miss Pound sat on her porch.

"Good morning, Anna," she said. She did not say anything to Big Hound. Big Hound jumped up and down with the lunch sack. Anna smiled. "Big Hound!" she said. "That lunch is for Dad!"

Anna and Big Hound passed Tim's house. Tim bounced his ball to Anna. Anna threw it back.

Big Hound didn't play ball. He pounced on the sack. Anna smiled. "Big Hound!" she said. "That lunch is for Dad!"

60

61

32C

HOUGHTON MIFFLIN
Reading
A Legacy of Literacy

Amazing Animals

A Park for Parkdale

by Patty Moynahan
illustrated by Bethann Thornburgh

Parkdale is a very nice town. It has houses and farms and stores. It has a market that sells nearly everything. It is a fine town, except for one thing. Parkdale has no park.

1

At the town meeting, Bart Horn stood up. "I have something important to say this morning," he told the town board. "We feel that a town named Parkdale needs a park."

Doctor Short nodded. So did Miss Martin.

2

Parkdale is a very nice town. It has houses and farms and stores and a market.

And now it has a park!

7

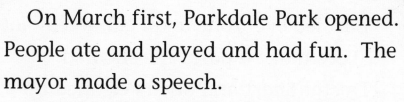

On March first, Parkdale Park opened. People ate and played and had fun. The mayor made a speech.

He said, "We are proud. See what can happen when everyone helps out!"

6

"Pardon me," said Cora Barkway, "but how will we pay for this park? We will need land. We will need someone to tend to this park."

The people began to think. Then Bart had an idea.

3

"Listen!" said Bart. "We will work together to make this park."

The people liked this smart plan.

"We'll start right now!" said Bart.

"I know a good spot for our park."

4

Bart led everyone to an old, weedy lot.

"Let's make a park!" he shouted.

Doctor Short and others cleaned up trash. Miss Martin planted a garden. More and more people came to help.

5

Arthur's Book

by Patty Moynahan
illustrated by John Manders

Arthur wanted to write his own book.
He had stacks and stacks of nice white
paper. He had three new pens. He had
lots of time for writing. Just one thing
was missing.

9

Arthur needed an idea. He started thinking and thinking.

"I'll tell a tale about a frightful sea creature," he told himself. "It could be a mixture of fact and fiction."

10

"That's it!" he yelled. He had an idea.

"My story will be about a cat that chases a dog. I know about that!" he said.

Then he went back to his desk and started to write.

15

Arthur felt that it might be helpful
to look at books. He picked up a book
from the fiction section of his shelf.
Just then, his dog and cat raced by.
They made him drop his book. That got
his attention.

14

Arthur looked out the window. He
saw his cat chasing his dog.

"How will this sea creature act?" he
asked. "That's the question."

Arthur kept thinking and thinking.

11

7D

Outside, his dog jumped up a tree.
Arthur did not see.

"My brain is starting to hurt," said
Arthur. "How hard can it be to get
an idea?"

Then Arthur looked back outside. He
saw his cat run up the tree. He saw his
dog in the tree. It was very funny.

"Sea creatures do not do funny things
like that!" Arthur said. "I need a new
idea."

12

13

Hank's Pandas

by Linda Dunlap
illustrated by Teri Sloat

My big brother is named Hank. He takes care of pandas at Animal Park. Hank tells me stories about his work. If I want, he takes me to see his pandas.

17

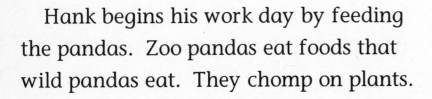

Hank begins his work day by feeding the pandas. Zoo pandas eat foods that wild pandas eat. They chomp on plants.

18

Mom cleans baby panda. Dad lends a hand. Then they go to sleep.

Hank and I go away quietly. We will be back to see the pandas soon.

23

10D

Pandas have nice fur. They groom it every day. Their light parts look as clean as snow.

Then Hank might weigh the new baby. It is so small! Hank can hold it in his arms.

22

19

Between his chores, Hank just watches the pandas. He likes to think and learn about pandas. Hank tells me what he sees.

Mom and her baby drink pond water. Dad sits close by.

20

21

Marta's Larks

by Linda Dunlap

illustrated by Christiane Beauregard

Marta was born on a farm. She has chores every day. The chore she likes best is feeding larks. Larks are birds that sing a lot. Marta likes to hear them each day.

25

In March, Marta works in her garden.
She sees larks try teamwork to turn a leaf.
"What is under that leaf?" Marta thinks.

26

Marta is a part of her larks' life. Larks
perch on her arms. Others eat seeds from
her hands. Marta is glad to have larks
for friends.

31

Marta likes watching larks at work. And larks feel safe when Marta is close. Marta would never harm her larks!

30

Marta picks up the leaf. A fat bug looks back at her! "Wow! Those larks are smart!" exclaims Marta. "I will start watching larks at work."

27

Marta sees larks working hard finding food. Even little larks eat lots of bugs. Larks swoop and dart in the sky. Hardly any bugs get away!

28

Marta sees larks working hard making nests. Larks pull bits of bark from large trees. They take blades of grass from the yard. Larks find torn yarn. They carry these things to a safe place. Then larks turn bark, grass, and yarn into nests!

29

Crow's Plan

by Melissa Blackwell Burke
illustrated by Cary Phillips

The animals at Oak Lake had a big problem. They met in the field to speak about it.

"Long ago, Oak Lake flowed clean," said Crow. "Now trash floats in it. We must make this lake flow clean once more."

33

"How can we help?" Toad croaked.

"We will make war on trash. Follow me!" said Crow.

Half the animals went around one side of Oak Lake. The rest went around the other side. They picked up trash and put it in trash cans.

34

So when you hear animals croak or moan or bellow, think about this tale. And don't throw trash!

39

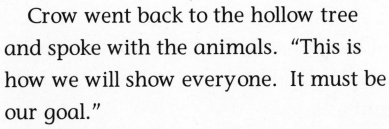

Crow went back to the hollow tree and spoke with the animals. "This is how we will show everyone. It must be our goal."

"Yes," they said. "You have our oath. If we see someone throw trash, we will croak or moan or bellow."

38

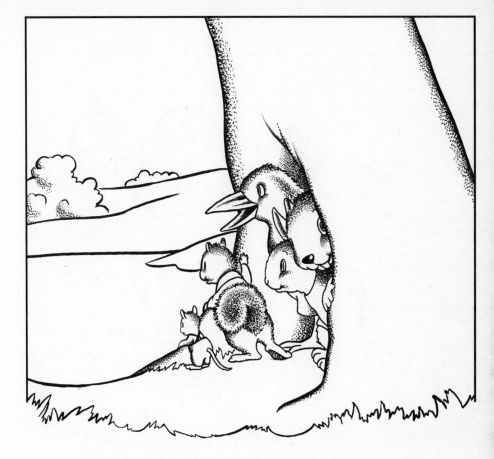

"This lake looks good and clean," Toad croaked. "Let's keep it this way."

"We can wait in this hollow tree," Crow said. "Then we will show everyone how to take care of the lake. It must be our goal."

35

Soon a raccoon family came to Oak Lake. The family ate a picnic in their rowboat. When they finished, the little raccoon tossed something. In a flash, Crow dove and got that trash in his beak before it hit Oak Lake.

36

Crow dropped that trash in a trash can. He flew back and bellowed at that family.

"I think I know why Crow is mad," the dad explained. "We won't throw trash again, fellow," he yelled up at Crow.

37

Brent Skunk Sings

by Melissa Blackwell Burke

illustrated by Laura Heliska-Beith

It was time for Brent Skunk to make his first trip to the dentist.

"This bird is the best dentist in this land," Granddad Frank said. "He is quite nice. When we go, he will clean your teeth and check them out. It will not hurt a bit."

41

Brent Skunk was afraid.

"This dentist visit won't take long,"
Granddad Frank said. "And you can
bring that yo-yo you like so much."

So Brent Skunk and Granddad Frank
went down to the dentist.

"I've got it!" Granddad Frank said.
"Brent can't pass up a chance to sing.
How about it, Brent?"

So Brent Skunk sang, and opened
wide.

The dentist counted and cleaned and
checked Brent's teeth.

It did not hurt a bit.

42

47

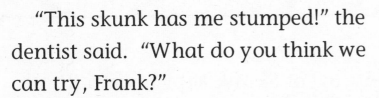

"This skunk has me stumped!" the dentist said. "What do you think we can try, Frank?"

"He opens wide when he laughs. We need to make him laugh. Can you do a stunt with that yo-yo?" Granddad Frank asked.

The dentist did three stunts. And Brent Skunk laughed, but with his hand over his mouth.

46

Brent Skunk and Granddad Frank sat in the waiting room.

When it was time to see the dentist, Granddad Frank found Brent Skunk behind a plant.

Granddad Frank yanked Brent Skunk out.

43

Granddad Frank set Brent Skunk down. Brent Skunk slumped.

Just then, the dentist came in.

"Brent Skunk, you'll be fine. We'll just count and clean and check those teeth. Let me get my lamp on so we can see. Open wide, please."

But Brent Skunk kept his mouth closed tight. He just sat there blinking.

"We'll get you a new toy with a string when we are through," the dentist said. "Now please open up."

Brent Skunk still kept his mouth closed tight.

44

45

24D

Family Time

My Sister Joan

by Becky Ward
illustrated by John Bendall-Brunello

My name is Kevin but my sister calls
me Buster. Her name is Joan.

It seems like trouble can find Joan no
matter where she is.

1

When Joan gets in a jam and needs help, she yells for me.

Last summer we went swimming at the lake. Joan ran around trying to catch grasshoppers. She never expected to get stung by a bee!

Big brothers must help younger sisters, so I tried to make Joan understand that she needed to stay away from trouble.

"What trouble, Buster?" she asked, as she gave me a big grape jelly hug.

2

7

We ran and found Joan standing in the middle of the bedroom in a pool of perfume.

The sitter cleaned up the glass, and I wiped up the perfume with water. Joan took a bath, but she still smelled awful.

"OUCH! Buster! Get that bad grasshopper!" yelled Joan.

I rubbed butter on her hand and explained to her about bees and stingers.

6

3

Another time we ate ice cream at Uncle Frank's house. When Joan tried to go outside, she let Uncle Frank's dog in. Joan yelled, "Buster! It's my ice cream. Help!"

I ran in. There was Joan with ice cream melting down her arm and a dog licking her face.

Last night, Mom and Dad went to a dinner party. I let the babysitter know that she must keep a close eye on Joan.

"We had better check on her," I said.

Then it happened. After a loud crash, Joan hollered, "Buster! Quick! I didn't mean to do it."

4

5

The Big Party Plan

by Becky Ward
illustrated by Elizabeth Wolf

"Children, get your coats on. We're going shopping in Willow Creek!" Mother called.

"Shopping? Willow Creek? Us?" The children thought Mother might be kidding. The Chang family lived on a farm and hardly ever went to Willow Creek, a town forty miles away.

9

"Yes, we're going shopping," said
Mother. "Did you forget that we're
throwing a party? We will get party
food and other things that we'll need.
I will let you do your own shopping
for gifts."

"Hooray!" cried the children,
running to get coats and snow boots.

10

Joan led Grandmother to the other
room.

"Happy Birthday!" everyone shouted.

When Grandmother saw the banner,
cake, and gifts, she hugged everyone.
Then she laughed and said, "This family
really knows how to throw a party!"

15

The next day, Father's red pickup truck came slowly up the driveway. Father and Grandmother got out. They had made a long trip in the snow. The children ran and greeted them on the steps.

"Grandmother, we've got something to show you!" cried Joan.

14

At Mister Sloan's store, the Changs roamed up and down the rows looking for gifts. Ann chose three sweet-smelling bars of soap. Chester found some yellow slippers. Joan picked out peppermint bath oil that would be nice to soak in. Paul got garden seeds for growing flowers.

"Those are nice choices," said Mother.

11

Mother got a pot roast, salad greens, cake mix, streamers, and balloons. They loaded everything up and started for home. Shopping put them in a happy mood, so they sang a few happy tunes as they drove down the snowy road.

When they got home, Mother said, "Let's get started. We've got loads to get done."

Mother had Paul and Joan blow up balloons. Then they hung streamers and a big "Happy Birthday" banner. Ann baked a yellow cake and Chester made a bowl of white frosting. Then the children wrapped gifts and made cards.

12

13

Lost and Found

by Anne Walker

illustrated by Devin Hunt

Lee woke up early. He looked in the red box under his bed.

Sparkle, his black and white cat, had not slept there. She had been missing for three days and nights.

"We'll just have to keep looking," Lee mumbled.

17

Nan and Fran came in. Fran was munching an apple.

"Lee," Nan said. "Can you help us? We don't know where we put our new pens."

"Yes, I can," replied Lee. "Then you can help me look for Sparkle."

18

"Look at that," Lee said softly. "Sparkle's got six brand new kittens!"

They looked at Sparkle's kittens. Three black kittens slept. Three white kittens stumbled on Sparkle's tail.

"Good job, Nan," he said. "I wouldn't have found Sparkle without your help."

23

Next, Fran, Nan, and Lee started
to hunt for Sparkle. Lee looked in
the kitchen.

Nan looked around the couch.
"Lee! Fran! Come !" she shouted.

22

Nan, Fran, and Lee went upstairs to
find the pens.

They looked on Nan's desk. They
looked under Fran's bed. They even
looked in the wastebasket.

"Let's ask Mom," Lee said. "She'll
know where we can look."

19

11E

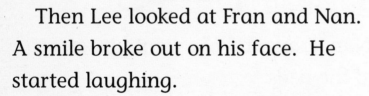

Then Lee looked at Fran and Nan.
A smile broke out on his face. He
started laughing.

"They'll never believe this," he
thought.

"What's making you laugh so hard?"
they asked. "Stop it!"

But Lee couldn't help himself.

20

At last Lee said, "Your pens are in
your hair!"

Nan fumbled in her hair and found
her pen. Then Fran found her pen in
her curls.

"Pens instead of bows," Nan said with
a chuckle. "We're going to start a new
trend!"

21

What Will Lester Be?

by Anne Walker

illustrated by April Hartmann

Lester's dad handed him a dinner plate. Lester dried it with a red cloth. He set it on the counter.

"Dad, what will I be when I grow up?" he asked quietly.

25

"You like cooking," Dad replied.

"Yes," Lester said. "I can make crust for pies. And I know how to use a roller." He stopped to think.

"That's it! I might be a baker," Lester shouted with joy.

"You are something right now, Lester," Grandmother said. "You are the best grandson in the world. So try not to grow up too fast," she said with a smile.

"You might be many things," said his grandmother.

"That's right!" exclaimed Lester. "I can cook, throw fast, read, and tell stories! I can be a lot of things when I grow up."

30

On Thursday, Lester threw three fast pitches. Ron missed them.

"I can throw fast!" Lester thought. "That's it! I might be a pitcher for big teams."

27

When Lester went hiking with his big sister, she said, "You might be a teacher like Miss Tuggle."

"Yes," Lester replied. "I could keep rulers, paper, and pens in my desk." Then he cried, "That's it! I might be a teacher!"

That afternoon, Lester looked at a book. His grandmother sat with him. "You like reading," she said.

"That's right," Lester replied. "I like reading and telling stories." He stopped to think.

"I might be a writer!" Lester exclaimed.

28

29

Aunt Lizzy Finds Her Cake

by Patty Moynahan
illustrated by Margeaux Lucas

Just look at this messy table! Willy and Pam are making a cake for Aunt Lizzy. Today is her birthday. This cake will be unlike other cakes. Aunt Lizzy must find this cake first. Then she can eat it!

33

Pam is writing notes with funny
clues. Aunt Lizzy must read each clue
to get her cake.

"Look inside a green fuzzy thing,"
reads the first clue. "Untie the string
and read the note."

Everyone went inside and ate ice
cream and cookies.

"I would not take a million dollars for
this day," said Aunt Lizzy. "Thanks for
my birthday surprise."

34

39

Aunt Lizzy found her cake. Benny had found the cake first. He did not need to read clues. Willy looked at Pam.

"I unlocked Benny's pen and forgot to lock it again."

38

Aunt Lizzy is looking for her cake. Her first clue was in a pair of slippers.

"Hurry!" urged the next note. "Go where flowers grow. It is unwise to waste time."

Aunt Lizzy rushed outside. Willy and Pam followed her.

35

"Go up three steps. A gift is waiting for you. Unwrap this gift and look inside."

36

Willy and Pam looked at each other and smiled. Aunt Lizzy found her last clue.

"Go where cars sleep. Look for a big white box."

37

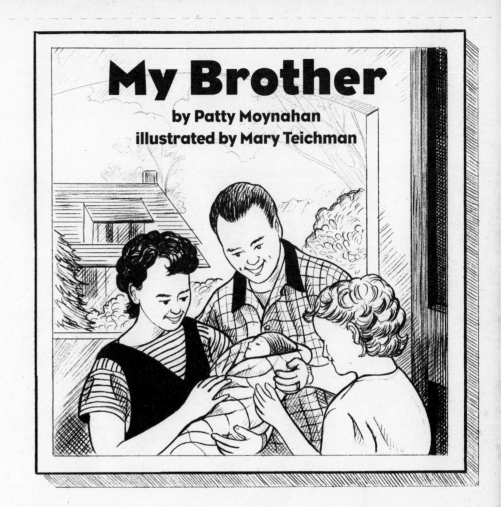

Jack Comes Home

Mom and Dad are home at last!
"What is in the bundle, Mom?"

"This is your new brother," she tells
me. "His name is Jack."

41

My new brother looks so little.
"Can I hold him, Dad? I'll be gentle."

42

We go for walks. I hold Jack's hand.
Jack is safe with me. We are brothers.
We are best friends.

47

Jack Is Three

We settle down for bed. "Will you read me this story?" asks Jack. This story is about an eagle. One day, I will teach my brother how to read.

46

Jack Is One

What is Jack thinking? Why does he wiggle? "Jack, hurry up and talk. Hurry up and walk."

Jack sees this bottle. Jack makes me giggle.

43

Jack Is Two

Jack is playing with his rattle. "Jack, where are your manners? Don't play at the table. Eat your scrambled eggs and apple!"

44

Mom lets me give Jack a bath. Jack likes to play with bubbles. "Jack! Quit splashing me!"

"Time to get out now. Or else you will wrinkle."

45

24E

Eight Daughters!

by Linda Dunlap

illustrated by Tamara Petrosino

In the Knox family there were eight daughters. Sissy Knox, at age fifteen, bossed them all around. She thought she knew just about everything! In fact, Sissy did know some things. She taught her younger sisters how to play right.

49

Then came the triplets — Peggy, Meggy, and Bessy. Peggy dressed like Meggy. Meggy dressed like Bessy. Bessy dressed like Peggy. Not even Dad knew which was which!

50

Now you know about the eight Knox daughters. Next time I might tell you about the eight Knox sons!

55

26E

Little Sara, number eight, was not very heavy yet. Sara crawled through the house on her knees. She gave bright smiles to each person. Kneel to play with Sara, and you might get a tight hug.

54

Child number five was Doreen. Doreen liked baking. She made muffins for the family. She kneaded and patted each morning. Then she baked and baked. Good smells filled the air. At night, the Knox family ate fresh muffins for dinner.

51

Myra, the sixth daughter, played drums. Neighbors held their heads every hour that Myra played. She knew how to keep a beat. But she played each tune with all her might. Her loud drumming made it hard to sleep at night.

Daughter number seven was Kate. Kate had a knack for getting in scrapes. She fell from tree limbs, skinning her knees. Her clothes, hands, and face were mainly muddy. Poor Kate always looked a sight!

52

53

28E

The Family Garden

by Linda Dunlap
illustrated by Linda Pierce

Each spring, Anna's family plants a garden. Everyone in her family helps.

57

Daddy plows the soil. His sure hands make nice, straight rows. It is good that Daddy is big. Plowing takes plenty of energy!

58

Now comes the best part! It is time to enjoy all that work! Anna's happy family eats many garden foods for dinner. Then Granny surprises them with fresh strawberry pie. You can see why gardening is such fun!

63

Then harvest starts! Anna's family spends sunny days picking good things to eat. Harvest baskets get packed and heavy. Everyone is thirsty, dirty, and happy.

Mom and Granny plant seeds. Each seed is placed gently in the soil. Then the seeds are topped with more soil. Most rows get seventy seeds. Planting can be hard work!

62

59

Finally, it is the children's turn. Anna and her brother make sure plants get what they need. They water the seedlings each day. They pull weeds, which take plants' food and air. Growing plants need air, sun, water, and food.

60

After many weeks, the garden is finally in bloom. It takes a long time, but plants need that much time to grow. You cannot hurry plants.

61

Talent Show

HOUGHTON MIFFLIN

Reading

A Legacy of Literacy

Our Classroom Zoo Book

by Linda Dunlap
illustrated by Mick Reid

Miss Moon's class made a zoo book.
It took us hours in the art room.

1

Miss Moon has cool art tools! We
drew with pencils and markers. We
found paints in every color, or hue. We
shared the paints to be fair. We also
used glue and paper. We even made
our own paste!

2

Miss Moon keeps our zoo book in our
room. We add new art too. That zoo
book makes us proud.

7

Sue drew zoo workers. One woman
was cleaning with a broom. Another
zoo helper was cooking food. It looked
like they were having a good time.

I drew a moose with droopy eyes.
That moose looked sad! I just knew I
would paint him blue.

6

3

Lou made a cool trout. She drew that trout with sparkling glue! Then she painted it gold inside the glue lines. She might paint a bunch of those trout!

Mansoor drew a very good goose. He saw a goose land on the ground. The goose stood very still. Mansoor looked at that goose while he drew. But then that goose flew away.

4

5

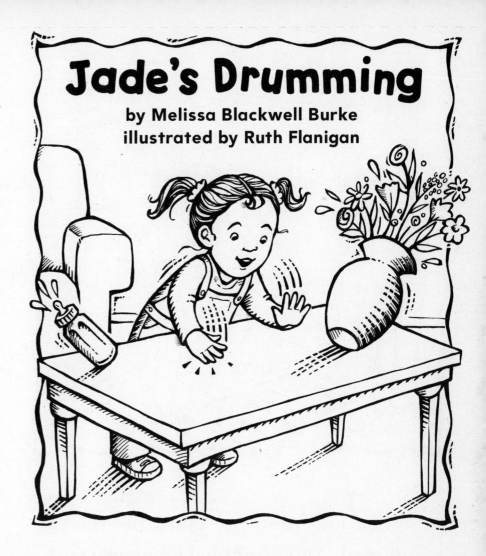

Jade's Drumming

by Melissa Blackwell Burke

illustrated by Ruth Flanigan

Tap! Tap! Tap! Tap! Tap! Tap!
When Jade was a baby, she began
drumming. She rapped and tapped
and patted on everything.

9

When Jade grew up some, she still drummed. She drummed when she was planning her day. She drummed when she was shopping. She drummed when she was sitting in the tub. Jade was forever drumming.

10

Jade waved to the crowd. The crowd stood up and clapped and clapped.

Jade's drumming made a lot of people very happy!

15

When Jade grew up, she did become a very good drummer. She asked her sister to go to a show. Her sister nodded, and off they went.

At the show, Jade did her drumming.

Her sister did not say that Jade was bugging her with so much drumming. Instead, she clapped and bragged, "That's my sister drumming!"

14

"You're bugging me with so much drumming," her sister would say.

But Jade never stopped. She just kept right on drumming.

"I like the sound," Jade would say. "Don't you like it too?"

11

At times her mother would say, "Jade, the baby is napping. Would you please stop drumming?"

Jade would say, "Yes, Mom, I will stop." Then she would drum outside.

12

When Jade and her sister rode the bus, Jade would do her drumming. It didn't matter if Jade's sister grabbed her drumsticks. Jade would just start patting her lap or tapping on the window.

"You're bugging me with so much drumming," her sister would say.

"I'm sorry," Jade would say. "I just like the sound so much."

13

Dwight the Knight

by Becky Ward
illustrated by John Manders

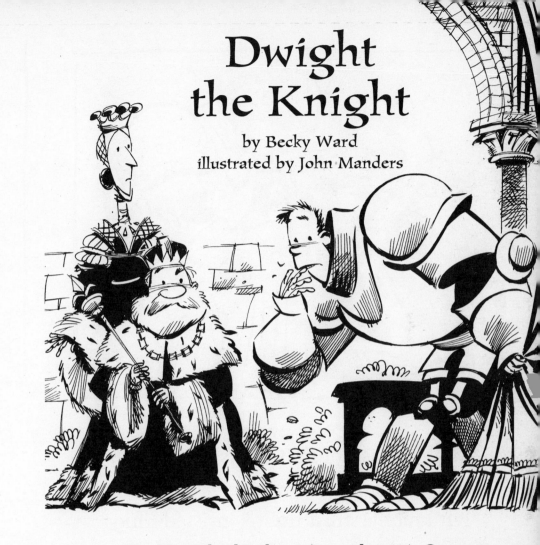

Sir Dwight had many talents. Queen Fair and King Mighty felt that Sir Dwight served them very well indeed. There was just one problem. Sir Dwight would not fight.

17

"My heart is not in it. This knight just can't fight," said Sir Dwight.

"But knights must fight," insisted King Mighty. "That is what knights do."

"Well, that is not what this knight does," said Sir Dwight. "Must I serve you in battle? I am able to serve you in so many other ways."

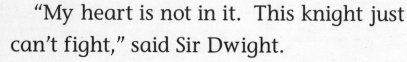

Then King Mighty spoke, "All right, Sir Dwight. It is not right to make you fight if you can't. Tell me, can you be a stay-at-home knight and serve us with your fine talents?"

Sir Dwight hugged King Mighty. "Yes, yes, yes! Yes I can!" he cried.

And that's what he did for the rest of his life!

18

23

"I can say the alphabet while I dance a jig. I can run like lightning each time you call. I can stitch you silk sheets that make sweet dreams each night," said Sir Dwight.

The knight went down on his knees. "I will try to grow wings and then take flight. But please, please, PLEASE don't make me fight," cried Sir Dwight.

22

"I can fix you a feast and do it up right. I'll stir up a fine beef stew and then bake you my best lemon pie," said Sir Dwight brightly.

"Sir Dwight, you are a fine cook," said Queen Fair. "But knights must go out and fight."

19

"I can tell you my best stories each night at bedtime. My mind is filled with wonderful tales. Some will delight you and others will fill you with fright," said Sir Dwight.

"Sir Dwight, we really like the way you tell tales," said King Mighty. "But knights must go out and fight."

"I can paint you pictures of beautiful sights," said Sir Dwight.

"And your paintings are delightful," said the queen. "But really, Sir Dwight, knights must go out and fight."

20

21

Who Drew the Cartoon?

by Becky Ward
illustrated by Len Epstein

When you look at a cartoon strip,
do you ever wonder who drew it?
An artist with lots of talent spent a
long time drawing that cartoon!

25

First, an artist has to think up a funny story to tell. Then he plans what will go in each drawing.

26

So you see, it is true. It takes time and talent to draw a cartoon. Can you think up an idea for a funny cartoon? Maybe you will invent a new comic strip!

31

Last, the artist chooses colors for the cartoon. He picks bright shades of blue, green, red, and yellow. Then he sends the comic strip to be printed.

Next the artist sketches the main things that go in each box of the cartoon strip. He uses pencil in case he goofs! He draws balloons and writes words in them, too.

30

27

Then the artist draws in the background. Some cartoon drawings need lines to show the walls in a room. Others need the moon or a few trees and clouds.

After that, the artist traces his pencil lines with ink. He uses fine pens, brushes, and art tools for adding lines and dots that look like shadows. An artist can cut out and glue patterns on the cartoon, too.

28

29

Will Holly Sing?

by Anne Walker
illustrated by Anne Kennedy

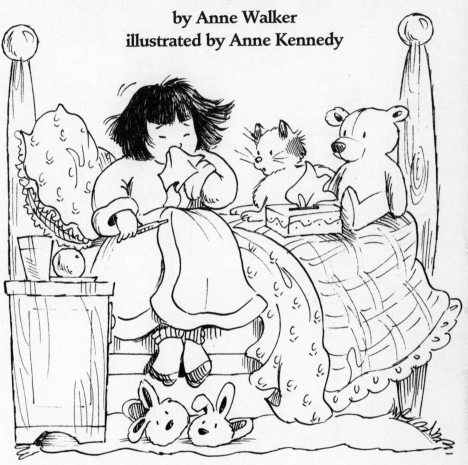

Holly sat up in bed.

"My cold is horrible," whined Holly.

Then she sneezed.

"I hope I can sing at the show."

33

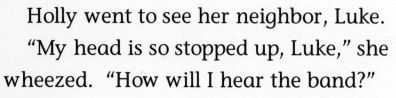

Holly went to see her neighbor, Luke.

"My head is so stopped up, Luke," she wheezed. "How will I hear the band?"

Luke gave her warm soup and some advice.

"Spend the day outside. The fresh air should help your head," he explained.

That night Holly sang in the show. Smiling, she said, "My first number is for Tom and Luke."

Then she sang "Good Friends."

34

39

"I'm super!" Holly replied. "My head feels better."

"So falling down fixed things up!" joked Tom.

Tom helped her inside his shop. He gave her some freshly baked apple pie.

Holly laced up her skates. She went skating in town, while her mom went shopping.

She glided past the drug store. She raced past Elmer's Hardware.

Soon she was smiling. But her head was still stopped up.

"Greetings, Holly," said Tom, the owner of Tom's Toys. He was placing three toy bears below a bench outside his shop.

"Good day," Holly replied, waving.

"Look out!" Tom shouted, but it was too late.

Crash! Holly wiped out just past Tom's store.

Tom raced to help Holly up.

She felt a little dazed. She stroked her scraped leg.

Then she shook her head.

"Are you all right?" Tom asked.

36

37

Fright Night

by Anne Walker
illustrated by Sarah Brittain

Miss Knight's class was getting set for Fright Night. They hung a banner outside the school.

"Fright Night will be the best night this year," cried Betsy. "I can't wait."

41

Many people came to see the show for Fright Night. Mothers and fathers found seats. Bright lights shone on the stage. Miss Knight said, "Steve Gilbert will go first."

The show ended with a tune sung by the whole class. The parents stood up and clapped. Everyone asked to have Fright Night again next year.

"We just might do that," sighed Miss Knight.

42

47

Sue and Shelly wore matching dresses with bright red tights. They tossed three glowing tubes back and forth like jugglers. Then Sue sang a spooky tune while Shelly played the sax.

Steve sat in the spotlight on Miss Knight's stool. He wore a green tie. He told a tale. In this tale a creature named Mighty Max lived in the woods. A brave boy made friends with this creature, and found out he was as gentle as a lamb.

46

43

Next, it was Sally's turn. Sally told about the high flight of six bats. She showed pictures of real bats. Then she yelled "BOO!" and ran off the stage.

Kenny dressed up for his spider dance. He was quite a sight. He wore a black cape cut in strips. The strips hung like a spider's legs. Kenny finished his dance and bowed.

44

45